THE MAID OF CEFN YDFA

JOAN PERKINS

Mrs Thomas brushed her wide hooped skirt and cast an impatient glance at the black-suited little man bent nearly double in front of her.

"Tell Mr Anthony Madock Senior I am here," she commanded loudly.

The man peered up at her through rimless glasses. "Certainly, madam. Who shall I say wishes to see him?"

"The Lady of Cefn Ydfa, of course." Surely the man had heard of her.

Her voice must have reached Anthony Maddock Senior who appeared at the door dressed more like a man of the church than a lawyer.

"Good morning, my dear lady. How delightful to see you. How kind of you to visit me in my chambers."

Mrs. Thomas swept past him wondering why solicitors called their offices 'chambers'.

"I have come to discuss the situation regarding the mortgage on Cefn Ydfa," she said haughtily. "As my lawyer, I expect you to advise me."

Mr. Maddock Senior retreated behind his large, mahogany, leather-topped desk.

"Quite so, madam." He paused and coughed gently. "The position is unchanged since our last meeting. There is a sum of

£500 due on the loan in one year."

"I can't pay it."

"Then, my dear lady, much of the land of the Cefn Ydfa estate will be claimed by those to whom the debt is owed."

Mrs. Thomas pursed her lips. "That must not be allowed to happen." She stood up. She was a small lady but the width of her skirts and the height of her hat made her seem taller. She pulled on her gloves. "We must discuss this matter more fully another time. Now I have to meet my daughter, Anne, who's returning on the noon stage from Bath. Her education there is finished and I must make arrangements for her to be presented at Court."

Anthony Maddock Senior tapped the desk with his finger tips. "These things cost money madam, but there may be a way, there may be a way," he repeated. "Perhaps you would be so kind as to invite my son and me to dine with you and your daughter at Cefn Ydfa?"

Mrs. Thomas was flattered. She was ambitious and since her husband's death, she had acquired land in every possible way for the Cefn Ydfa estate. Crofters were finding it difficult to make a living and compete with the new farming methods used by the large landowners and she had been able to buy several smallholdings at very good prices. Now she wanted social recognition and a man of Anthony Maddock's standing could help.

Anne Thomas was unaware of her beauty, the pale oval face with its small pert nose, smiling mouth and large blue, long-lashed eyes. During her journey her hair had escaped from her hat and curled around her face. She was also unaware of the plan taking shape in the mind of the rather odd-looking man standing beside her mother waiting for the coach to arrive.

"I would like you to meet Mr. Anthony Maddock Senior. He has been our family adviser for a long time but since you've been away so much, I don't think you have met him."

"My pleasure," said Mr. Maddock and kissed her hand. "My son and I have wanted to meet you for a long time."

"Mr. Maddock and his son are coming to dine with us at Cefn Ydfa," Mrs. Thomas explained hastily.

Anne disliked Mr. Maddock Senior instinctively, feeling that he was insincere. She did not trust the pale grey eyes that watched her face so closely and she was glad when her mother said that they must hurry home.

About two miles ouside the village, both women heard another horse being ridden hard behind them. Looking over her shoulder, Mrs. Thomas recognised the masked figure of a local highwayman who had held up several wealthy people in the neighbourhood.

"Do not resist, mother," said Anne, fearing for her mother's safety as the masked rider and his horse blocked their path.

Mrs. Thomas had already handed over her purse when a young man, his tawny red hair flowing freely about his head, rode into the group and with one fierce blow, hit the highwayman off his horse.

The thief dropped the purse, scrambled to his feet and ran as fast as he could, his horse cantering after him.

"Your purse, madam."

"Thank you, Will Hopkin. How fortunate that you happened to come by."

"Not really, Mrs. Thomas. I saw the rascal watching you in the village when you were waiting for the coach with Anthony Maddock. I guessed what he was up to and followed you."

Mrs. Thomas had recovered her composure. "Mr. Anthony Maddock Senior," she corrected him. "We are most grateful for your help. It is a disgrace that the ruffian has not been caught."

"Do you remember me Will?" Anne asked shyly.

"Of course, although you've grown up since you used to chase me around the barn at Cefn Ydfa."

Anne blushed, partly at the warm admiration in his brown eyes and partly at the memory of their innocent childhood games.

"There is a tile off the roof at the Great House. You must come and repair it. Also, I require three new pigsties built," said Mrs. Thomas, stiffly.

"I'll come to Cefn Ydfa in the next day or two," Will promised Mrs. Thomas but his gaze was on Anne.

Mrs. Thomas decided against offering Will a guinea as a reward for rescuing them. He had too many airs and graces for a mere tiler. He also collected the local taxes used to provide for the poor and had a reputation as a poet. He had learned to read at the circulating school held occasionally in the porch of the church and was, thought Mrs. Thomas, altogether too big for his boots.

Mrs. Thomas did not care to be beholden to someone she considered to be beneath her station in life.

Nodding goodbye to the young man, she gathered the reins of her horse in her hand and rode on and Anne followed her.

Happiness for Anne Thomas was to be found in the hills and valleys and streams around Llangynwyd. She loved to ride her horse and to walk leaving the wind to free her dark, curly hair and touch her lips and cheeks with pink.

She found her thoughts turning to the young man who had dealt so effectively with the highwayman and was delighted when he came to Cefn Ydfa to begin the work requested by her mother.

Will's singing woke Anne one morning and wrapping a shawl around her shoulders against the chill, she slipped out into the woods. The grass was wet with dew and the trees were still wrapped in their blankets of mist.

Anne stopped suddenly as a twig cracked behing her. At first she could see nothing then the swirling vapour took shape and an old woman, as fragile as the mist itself, came towards her. Scrawny hands clutched at the folds of a ragged black shawl about her shoulders; a long bony finger beckoned to Anne.

"Come here, pretty miss," she called. "There is much pain and unhappiness coming to you. You will marry a man you do not love and your grave is waiting for you."

Anne recoiled in horror. But even as she watched, the mist stirred and the old crone had vanished.

Back in the warmth of Cefn Ydfa, Anne dismissed the warning as nonsense. She was virtually her own mistress and could marry any man she chose. She could hear Will Hopkin clambering over the roof and a smile played around her lips.

Will's skill as a tiler was well known with each tile set in mortar but no mortar showing. He worked quickly and had soon completed the work on the roof.

At midday, Will ate in the kitchen at Cefn Ydfa with the housekeeper, Jane the Chambermaid, Rhys the shepherd and a milkmaid: bacon and wheaten bread, better fare than the oatcakes and barley bread of the poorer crofters.

He was pleased when Anne joined them and noticed that the staff talked freely with her and that she laughed and teased them.

The cost of the repair was two shillings but he also collected a tax of five shillings for the care of the poor. He asked for a quill, ink and paper and wrote out the receipt in a steady hand.

Mrs. Thomas felt annoyed that this boy should be able to write while she could not.

The roof finished, Will started work on the pigsties. Anne watched the sure hands and the strong young body, tanned by the sun and wind.

When the day's work was done, they walked and talked. Anne discovered Will liked poetry and wrote verses and she gave him her leather bound copy of Shakespeare.

Anne's maid, Jane, was to marry soon and listening to Will reading aloud, Anne wished she could be betrothed to Will.

Mrs. Thomas was so busy preparing for the dinner party for Anthony Maddock Senior and his son that she did not realise that Anne and Will had fallen deeply in love.

Anthony Maddock Junior was more pompous and more of a bore than his father; full of his own importance, he liked the sound of his own voice. Anne obviously thought the young man ridiculous and Mrs. Thomas was glad she had invited her brother, the Rev. Price.

"Anne take Anthony to see the grounds," suggested her mother when the meal was over.

"The estate must not be broken up," said Rev. Price when the young couple had left the room.

"That may be difficult to avoid if the money is not available," commented Anthony Maddock Senior leaning back in his chair more comfortably after the excellent meal he had just enjoyed.

Rev. Price took out his pipe and silently asked his sister's permission to smoke. "Anne must make a suitable marriage."

Anthony Maddock tried to conceal his delight. "You have someone in mind?"

'Your son." Rev. Price exhaled a cloud of smoke. He always believed in speaking his mind. "The advantages are obvious. Cwmyrisgla land the other side of the mountain joined with Cefn Ydfa land here. Together they would make a very fine estate."

"I should be interested to see the sort of marriage settlement you have in mind," said Anthony Maddock Senior cautiously.

Mrs. Thomas sighed with relief and went to refill the Cefn Ydfa silver tankards with fresh ale. The situation was proceeding very satisfactorily.

That was more than could be said for Anne and Anthony Maddock Junior. He could not understand why this young country girl should be so cold towards him and treat him with such disdain. He rated himself highly in the marriage stakes and were it not for the Cefn Ydfa estate, he would not give her a second

glance. Although, she was, he had to admit, a rather pretty wench.

Anne missed Will. She found Anthony Maddock Junior vain, boring and stupid. He had little conversation other than vague distasteful references to past romantic conquests.

The first Wednesday after May Day was Mercher Amodau - Covenant Wednesday. On this day, a fair was held at which people looking for work could be hired for a year.

Since Anne's maid, Jane, was to marry Jenkin Dafydd, Anne wanted to choose her replacement.

Men and women, lads and lasses of all ages and occupations had gathered at the Fair: shepherds, cowmen, ploughmen, hedgers, ditchers, dairymaids, housemaids and seamstresses. Not all sought to be hired. The Fair was a great social event with dancing and games in the evening and the young ones pairing off.

Anne soon chose a new maid, Mari Powell, and Mrs. Thomas set off to the Castell to visit a cousin, leaving Anne to make her own way back to Cefn Ydfa.

On the way, Anne stopped at Will's.home, Corner House, tethering her house to the gate post.

"Come in Anne," invited Will's mother. "You have grown into a beautiful young woman. Will talks of little else but you and I can understand why."

It was there that Will found them, drinking tea and eating

oatmeal cakes with fresh butter.

Will looked at Anne's blue eyes, at the dark curls escaping from a small Puritan cap and knew he had met the woman he wanted to marry.

"You had better ride back to Cefn Ydfa with Anne and escort her safely home," suggested Mrs. Hopkin.

Riding through the lanes at Anne's side, Will thought life was so good he would never be happier.

Two weeks later, Jane and Jenkin were married. In the evening, after the wedding feast, a small group of men organised by Will set off for the glade at Gilfach Isaf and the building of a *ty un nos,* a one-night house, for the newly weds began. By custom, if the house was built and occupied by Jenkin and Jane by the morning, it belonged to them.

By daybreak, the newly weds were asleep in front of their own hearth.

Soon everyone knew about the *ty un nos* and Mrs. Thomas in particular was furious. She considered that the land was not enclosed and was part of the Cefn Ydfa estate.

She was even more angry when Will suggested that she test her claim in the court saying that if she had a right to the land, Jenkin would pay rent.

At last the terms of the marriage settlement were agreed and

Anthony Maddock Junior wrote a formal offer of marriage to Anne.

When she read the letter, Anne's heart filled with horror and disbelief and she fled to Bryn y Fro where Will was waiting for her. In his arms, Anne vowed that she would marry no one but him.

Will wanted to confront Mrs. Thomas and take Anne away with him. But Anne felt sure that she could persuade her mother that she did not want to marry young Maddock and that her mother would allow her to marry the man she loved.

Will's distrust of the Maddocks was confirmed when he heard that Anthony Maddock Junior, now the legal representative of Mrs. Thomas and the Cefn Ydfa estate, planned to test the right of Jenkin to the *ty un nos* at the Court Leet.

Will represented the young couple and the court decided that they had not broken any law and could not be evicted.

Refused by the woman he wanted to marry, humiliated in law, Anthony Maddock Junior vowed vengeance on the man he thought responsible for all his problems: Will Hopkin.

Anne's mother, determined to keep the lovers apart, confined her daughter to her room.

At first, Anne and Will communicated secretly by letter but then Mrs. Thomas intercepted their love letters. Thus, each

continued to write and wait in vain for a reply.

One day, an old packman came to Cefn Ydfa. There was great excitement in the house and Mrs. Thomas allowed Anne to buy some ribbons. As the man pressed the bundle of ribbons into her hand, he looked deeply into her eyes. Anne trembled realising that the man was her lover, Will Hopkin.

Mrs. Thomas became more and more angry at her daughter's stubborn refusal to make what the older woman regarded as a "good match". Anne's pleas that she loved Will Hopkin had no effect.

The once loving, kind mother was completely obsessed with the idea that Anne must marry Maddock.

Mari was forbidden to speak to Anne who became paler and thinner as the days passed.

Anthony Maddock Junior continued to come to Cefn Ydfa to press his suit.

"I will never marry you," Anne said defiantly. " You are wasting your time."

Anne found the smiling, fawning young man more distasteful than his bullying father and her rejection only served to make both men more determined to subdue her.

Fearing that Anne would come of age and be her own mistress before the marriage was finalised, Mrs. Thomas locked Anne in

the dungeon, hoping that his would break her spirit.

It was a low, damp, dark room with water trickling between the cold stone of the walls. What little light entered the room, did so through a small window so dusty that it was almost indistinguishable from the wall. The wooden bed was hard and there was no blanket.

It seemed as if her mother was intent on destroying her daughter.

Anthony Maddock Senior too grew more impatient. It was unthinkable that this young minx should make fools of them all.

He forged a receipt claiming it had been signed by Will in return for fifty guineas, payment for agreeing not to see Anne again.

Anne looked scornfully at Anthony Maddock Senior and his son.

"It's a forgery," she cried, defiantly. "Let me examine it."

"We have no wish to distress you further," the older man said and tore the document into small pieces.

Anne felt as if her heart was breaking.

It had been a clever ploy. Alone in her prison Anne began to wonder if Will had really forsaken her.

She found it difficult to distinguish between fantasy and reality, between truth and deceit. Sometimes she thought Will

was in her prison with her and she cried out to him. At other times, she thought he had married someone else and she wept piteously.

Her mother had removed anything that might be used to write with but the window in the dungeon was cracked and a slither of glass lay on the floor beneath it. Anne picked up the glass and pricked her finger until the blood flowed. Using the glass dipped in her blood, she scratched out a last desperate message on the wall to her lover.

That was her last pathetic appeal. The next morning she was forced to sign the marriage contract.

Barely aware of what was happening, Anne was taken to the church of Llangynwyd. Supported by the groom lest she fall to the ground, she whispered her marriage vows.

At first Anne tried to be a good wife but Anthony Maddock treated her like an unpaid servant. He liked to show her off to his friends as though she was a bargain he had purchased. Mrs. Thomas spent little time at Cefn Ydfa because her son-in-law made her unwelcome.

Maddock still sought revenge on Will Hopkin and he persuaded Mrs. Thomas to sign an order giving him permission to evict Jane and Jenkin by whatever means he chose. He sent his bailiff who knocked Jenkin senseless. Then curiously, the bailiff disappeared.

Will hurried to the home of Jenkin and Jane. There he met Anne, helping to nurse the injured Jenkin.

Within minutes, the two were in each other 's arms, their love burning as brightly as before.

Anne explained that her husband was unfaithful to her and she hoped that she and Will could find some way to be together. It was not to be.

Maddock accused Will of murdering the bailiff and Will fled to Bristol, working and waiting until he could come back to Llangynwyd and clear his name.

Some twenty months later, Will learned that Jenkin's father had confessed to killing the bailiff because of the way the man had treated his son.

Will also heard that Anne was very sick and was calling for him. He returned immediately to Cefn Ydfa.

At first, Anne did not know him. He cradled her in his arms as the fever and cough wracked her frail body. Too weak to remove her wedding ring, she begged Will to take it lest she should have no peace in her grave.

In 1741, a man was seen examining the tombstone where Anne was buried. He sat on her grave, head bowed, until darkness

covered the graveyard. A few days later he died. When his body was being prepared for burial, Anne's wedding ring was found on a chain at his neck. He was buried in the churchyard. At last, the lovers were together.

ISBN 1 85122 103 4

DOMINO BOOKS LTD.,
P O Box 78,
Swansea SA1 1YT.